Ottorino Respighi

LAUD TO THE NATIVITY

(Lauda per la Natività del Signore)

for

Solo Voices, Mixed Chorus and Instrumental Ensemble

Piano Reduction by
Guido Zuccoli

Text attributed to Jacopone da Todi
English Version by Harold Heiberg

133002

RICORDI

Suggestions for Staging
of the

LAUD TO THE NATIVITY

The stage should represent an Italian manger of the 15th or 16th century and in its essential details can draw inspiration from the paintings and frescoes of that period.

The cast of characters for this work are: the Angel(coloratura soprano), the Virgin Mary (mezzo-soprano) and the Shepherd (tenor). That of Joseph is a non-singing role.

The chorus (of Angels, Shepherds, etc.) and the instrumental ensemble should remain out of sight. The Angels and Shepherds should be performed by dancers or mimes, who will assume graceful poses according to the words sung by the chorus.

It is also suggested that instead of a graphic representation of the Child being placed between the Virgin Mary and Joseph, that there be some straw, only, in the manger, lighted from the inside. In the last scene, while the rest of the stage dims little by little, the brightness of the straw gradually becomes stronger, so to light the faces of the Virgin and Joseph, kneeling in an adoring attitude.

ELSA RESPIGHI

INSTRUMENTATION

2 Flutes (Fl. 2 doubles Piccolo)
Oboe
English Horn
2 Bassoons
Triangle
Piano (1 Piano-4 hands)

Duration: 25 min.

Orchestral materials available on rental from the publisher.

To Count Guido Chigi Saracini

LAUD TO THE NATIVITY

(Lauda per la Natività del Signore)

(Text attributed to Jacopone da Todi)

English Version by
Harold Heiberg

OTTORINO RESPIGHI
(1930)

The Angel (to the Shepherds)
L'Angelo (ad Pastores)

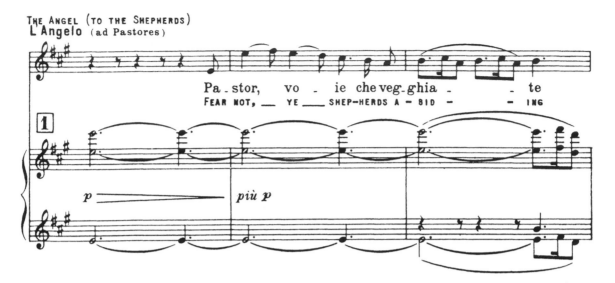

Pa_stor, vo_ie che veg_ghia_ _te
FEAR NOT, __ YE __ SHEP-HERDS A-BID- __ING

L'Angelo (THE ANGEL)

so_ _vra la greg_ _gia____ en qui_sta re_
HERE ____ ON __ THE HILL- __SIDES ____ OF JU-DE-A'S

L'Angelo (THE ANGEL)

gio_ _ne;____ I vo_str'oc_ _chi le_
RE- __GIONS,____ LO, I BRING ____ YOU A

4

L'Angelo (THE ANGEL)

Ed a vo _ ie van_ge_liz _ _ zo gau_dio fi _ _ _
TO A VIR - GIN IS THE SAV- -IOR THE _ A - NOINT- - -

cresc.

L'Angelo (THE ANGEL)

_ no, _____ Ch'è na _ to el Ge_su_
- ED, _____ CHRIST JE - SUS, WHOM GOD AP -

mf _____ *f*

L'Angelo (THE ANGEL)

_ i _ no fi _ gliuol _ de Di _ o, _____ per
- POINT - ED TO COME_ FROM HEAV- -EN, _____ FROM

cresc.

L'Angelo (THE ANGEL)

vo _ ie sal_var_____ man_da _ _ _ _ _
HEAV'N _____ THAT YE MIGHT _____ BE SAV - - -

ff dim.

p

L'Angelo (THE ANGEL)

_to._____
- èD. _____

Soprani

pp

E _ de ciò ve _ dò en se _ gno Ch'en vi_le
AND _____ THIS CHILD, PURE _ AND HO _ LY, SENT BY THE

Mezzi Soprani

pp

E _ de ciò ve _ dò en se _ gno Ch'en vi_le
AND _____ THIS CHILD, PURE _ AND HO _ LY, SENT BY THE

Tenori

pp

E de ciò _____ ve dò _ en
AND THIS CHILD, _____ SO PURE _ AND

Bassi

pp

E de ciò _____ ve _____ dò en
AND THIS CHILD, _____ PURE _____ AND

rall:.................

3 Poco piu lento ♩. = 72

stal_la è na _ to el po_ve_rel _ _ lo, E non se fa de_
LORD A-GAINST E-VIL TO BAT- -TLE, LIES IN A STA-BLE
stal_la è na _ to el po_ve_rel _ _ lo, E non se fa de_
LORD A-GAINST E-VIL TO BAT- -TLE, LIES IN A STA-BLE
se - gno che in vi_le stal_ la che in vi_le
HO - LY, SENT BY THE FA - THER, SENT BY THE
se - - gno che in vi_le
HO - - LY, SENT BY THE
poco cresc:
_sde _ gno Giace _ re en mez _ zo al buo_ve e l'a_ se_
LOW - LY WITH-IN-A MAN - GER, A-MONG THE SHEEP AND THE
_sde _ gno Giace _ re en mez _ zo al buo_ve e l'a_ se_
LOW - LY WITH-IN-A MAN - GER, A-MONG THE SHEEP AND THE
stal - la è na - to el po - ve-rel - lo.
LORD A-GAINST E-VIL TO DO BAT - TLE,
poco cresc:
stal - la è na - to el po_ve_rel - lo.
FA - THER A-GAINST E-VIL TO BAT - TLE,
p
mp

f
so - vra el man - gia - to - io, l'ha rin - chi -
f LIN - EN HAS GEN - TLY BOUND HIM, MAR - Y SO
so - vra el man - gia - to - io, l'ha rin - chi - na - to, l'ha rin - chi -
LIN - EN GEN - TLY BOUND HIM, MAR - Y HAS GEN - TLY, MAR - Y SO
f
- nel - lo. La mam - ma en vil pan -
f CAT - TLE. TO SHIELD THE CHILD FROM THE
en mez - zo al buo - ve
MAN - GER, A - MONG THE
f
f
- na - to so - vra el man - gia - to - io.
GEN - TLY IN LIN - EN HAS BOUND HIM;
mp
- na - to so - vra el man - gia - to - io. De
GEN - TLY IN LIN - EN HAS BOUND HIM; HIS
- cel - lo l'ha rin - chi - na - to so - vra el man - gia - to -
BREEZ - ES, MAR - Y SO GEN - TLY IN LIN - EN HAS BOUND
e l'a - se - nel -
SHEEP AND THE CAT -
mf dim.

De fie - no è'l co - ver - to - io, Ed è de -
His blan - ket, the hay a - round Him, Thus art Thou
fie - no, de - fie - no è'l co - ver - to - io, Ed è de -
blan - ket, His blan - ket, the hay a - round Him, Thus art Thou
- io. De fie - no è'l co - ver - to - io, Ed è de -
Him; His blan - ket, hay a - round Him. Thus art Thou
- lo. De fie - no È
- tle. His blan - ket is
4
L'Angelo (The Angel)
Pa -
Fear
dim.
- scie - so co - sì hu - mi - lia - to, ed è de - scie - so co - sì hu - mi -
come down to earth, bles - sèd Je - sus, Thus art Thou come down to earth, bles - sèd
el co - ver - to - io, el co - ver -
the hay a - round Him, the hay a -
poco rit:

10

L'Angelo (THE ANGEL)

L'Angelo (THE ANGEL)

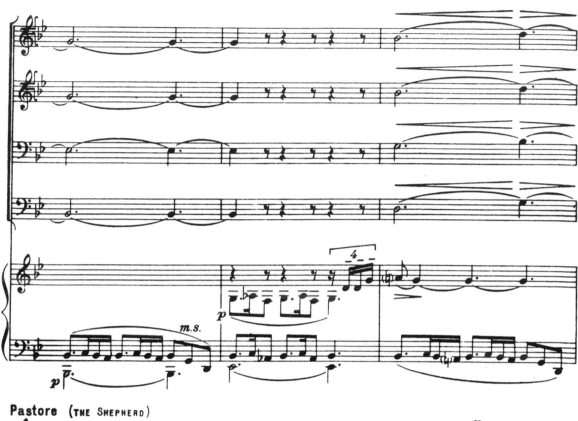

Pastore (THE SHEPHERD)

sempre a bocca chiusa

(CLOSED LIPS)

(CLOSED LIPS)

Segnor, tu sei de_
O LORD, THOU HAST DE-

7 **Andante** ♩=69

Pastore (THE SHEPHERD)

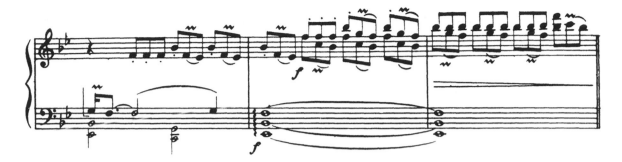

PASTORES ANTE PRAESEPIO (THE SHEPHERDS AT THE MANGER)

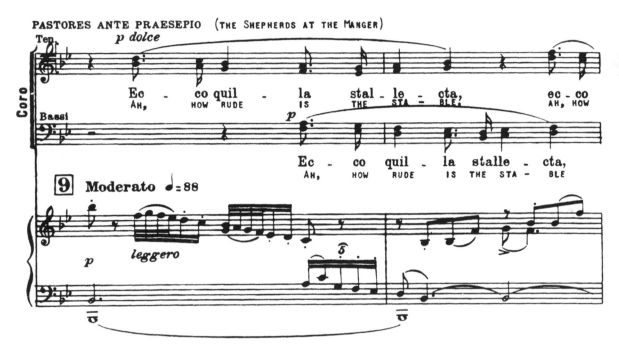

Ec - co quil - la stal - le - cta, ec - co
AH, HOW RUDE IS THE STA - BLE; AH, HOW

Ec - co quil - la stalle - cta,
AH, HOW RUDE IS THE STA - BLE

9 Moderato ♩=88

quil - la stal-le - cta; ve - dem-ce lo fan -
RUDE IS THE STA - BLE WHERE ____ FAST A-SLEEP THE

ve - dem-ce lo fan - ti - no
WHERE ___ FAST A - SLEEP THE IN - FANT

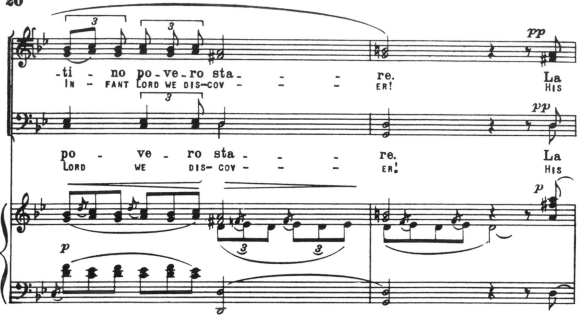

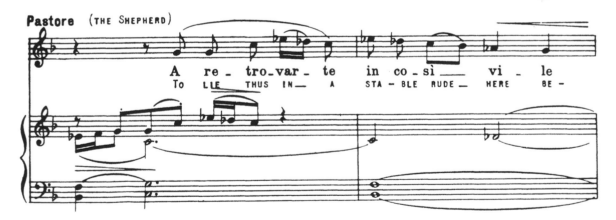

Maria (MARY)

O My

13 Lento ♩.=60

p dolce

Maria (MARY)

car_ dol_ce mio fi _ glio, Da me se'na _ to_ sì po _ ve_rel_lo!
CHILD,_SWEET BE THY SLUM-BER. THOUGH THOU MUST LIE— POOR— HERE IN— A MAN-GER,

Maria (MARY)

Jo_se_pe el ve _ chia_ rel _ _ _ lo Quil_ ch'è tuo
BRIGHT AN-GELS WITH-OUT NUM _ _ _ BER HOV — ER A—

Maria (MARY)

bai _ lo, qui s'è a _ dor_ menta _ to.
ROUND THEE, GUARD- ING THEE—FROM DAN — GER.

p

cresc.

Maria (MARY)

Fi-gliuol, gau-dio per-fe - cto,_____ ched
My Son, with what af - fec - tion _____ I

Maria (MARY)

i sen-ti - e a la tu-a na-ti-vi-ta - te! Stren-
gaze up-on _____ Thee! Filled-with awe on Thy birth I pon - der! Be-

Maria (MARY)

-gen-dom-et' al pe-cto, Non me cu-ra - va de nul-la po-ver-ta - de,
-hold-ing Thy per-fec-tion, I am re-moved far from pov-er-ty and sad-ness.

(MARY)
Maria

a tempo tan - ta su-a - vi-ta - de Tu si me da -
My _ heart- is filled-with glad - ness, For- joy _ far great-

14

Maria (MARY)

ie de quil gau _dio e_ter_no, O fi_gliuol_ te _ ne_
-ER THAN MY_ JOY MA - TER - NAL COMES FROM THEE,_ CHILD ___ OF

Maria (MARY)

-rel _ _lo!
WON - - DER!

Soprani

_pp_

O fon_te d'a_o_li_men_to___
O FOUN - TAIN OF JOY E - TER - NAL,

Mezzi Sopr.

_pp_

O fon_te d'a_o_li-
O FOUN - TAIN OF JOY E-

Tenori

_pp_

O fon_ _ _te d'a_o_li_men _
O FOUN - - TAIN OF JOY E - TER -

Baritoni

_pp_

O fon_te d'a_o_li-
O FOUN - TAIN OF JOY E -

Bassi

_pp_

O fon_ _te
O FOUNT ___ OF ___

rall:.................... a tempo

_p_

Maria (MARY)

Te vo io fasciare con quisto mio pan_cel _ lo,　O figliuo_lo po_ve_
THOUGH NA-KED HE LIES IN THE HAY IT WILL NOT GRIEVE _ HIM,　IF WE ON - LY WILL BE-

Che stanno in sel_va col_la greggia tan _ ta.　El figliuol ammanta,
OUR FLOCKS UN-GUARD-ED STAND, WE CAN-NOT TAR - RY.　NOW NO LONG-ER CARE WE

Che stanno in sel_va col_la greggia tan _ ta.　El figliuol ammanta,
OUR FLOCKS UN-GUARD-ED STAND, WE CAN-NOT TAR - RY.　NOW NO LONG-ER CARE WE

Che stanno in sel_va col_la greggia tan _ ta.　El figliuol ammanta,
OUR FLOCKS UN-GUARD-ED STAND, WE CAN-NOT TAR - RY.　NOW NO LONG-ER CARE WE

Maria (MARY)

_rel _ lo,　Co l'ha promesso il pate tuo bi_
- LIEVE - ON　HIM,　THIS HEAVN-LY IN_FANT WHOM THE FA-THER

che non a _ li _ ta el fie_no,　sua carne pu_
FOR THE COLD: WE HAVE BE-HELD HIM, _ THE IN-FANT JE -

che non a _ li _ ta el fie_no,　sua carne pu_
FOR THE COLD: WE HAVE BE-HELD HIM, _ THE IN-FANT JE -

che non a _ li _ ta el fie_no,　sua carne pu_
FOR THE COLD: WE HAVE BE-HELD HIM, _ THE IN-FANT JE -

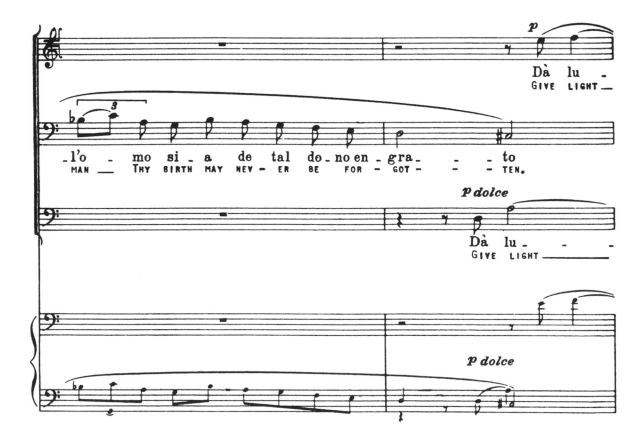

20

Allegretto ♩·= 72 (in uno)

te, O Si - re del ciel, del
THEE, O FA - THER ON HIGH, ON
Glo - ri a lau - de o - no - re a te, o
GLO - RY AND HON - OR AND PRAISE UN - TO THEE, O
te, O Si - re del cie - lo on -
THEE, O FA - THER IN - HEAV - EN, THOU
Glo - ri - a, o - no - re a
GLO - RY, - PRAISE - AND HON - OR - TO -
ciel
HIGH
Si - re del ciel, o Si - re del
FA - THER ON HIGH, O FA - THER ON
- ne - poten - te, o Si - re del
GOD AL - MIGHT - Y, O FA - THER ON
te, Si - re del ciel on - ne - po -
THEE, FA - THER ON HIGH, THOU GOD AL -

52

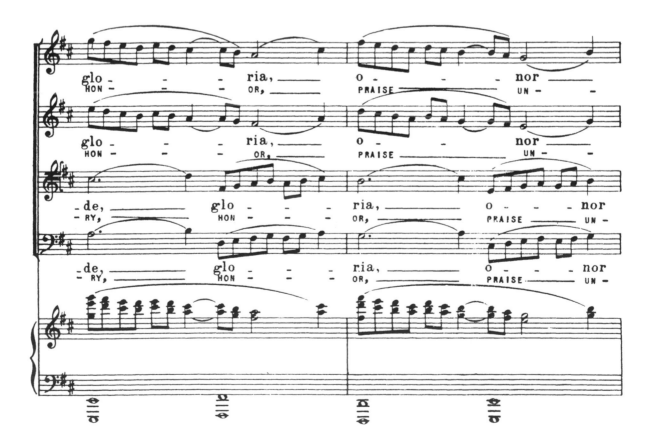

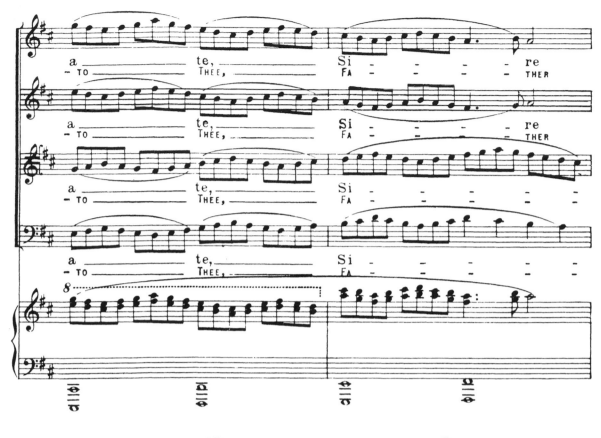

sol per tuo pia_ce - re.
CHILD — OF — HEAV'N-LY BEAU - - - TY.
-ve - re, Ma sol per tuo pia_ce - re.
DU - TY, O — CHILD — OF — HEAV'N-LY BEAU - TY.
tu - o do - ver, Ma per tu - o pia - ce - re.
DU - TY, O CHILD, O — CHILD — OF — HEAV'N-LY BEAU - TY.
— el buon — vo - le - - -
— GOOD WILL — TO - WARD
p
Noi — te lau_diam, Si - gno - - - re, Glo - ri - fi -
LAUD — WE THY NAME, EX - TOL — THEE, LORD OF ALL -
Noi te lau - diam, Si - gno - - - re, Glo_ri - fi -
LAUD WE THY NAME, EX - TOL — THEE, LORD OF ALL
Noi te lau - diam, Si - gno - - - re, — Glo_ri - fi -
LAUD WE THY NAME, — EX - TOL — THEE, — LORD OF ALL
-re, — A — chi ha —
MEN, — PEACE — ON EARTH, —
30

L'Angelo (THE ANGEL)

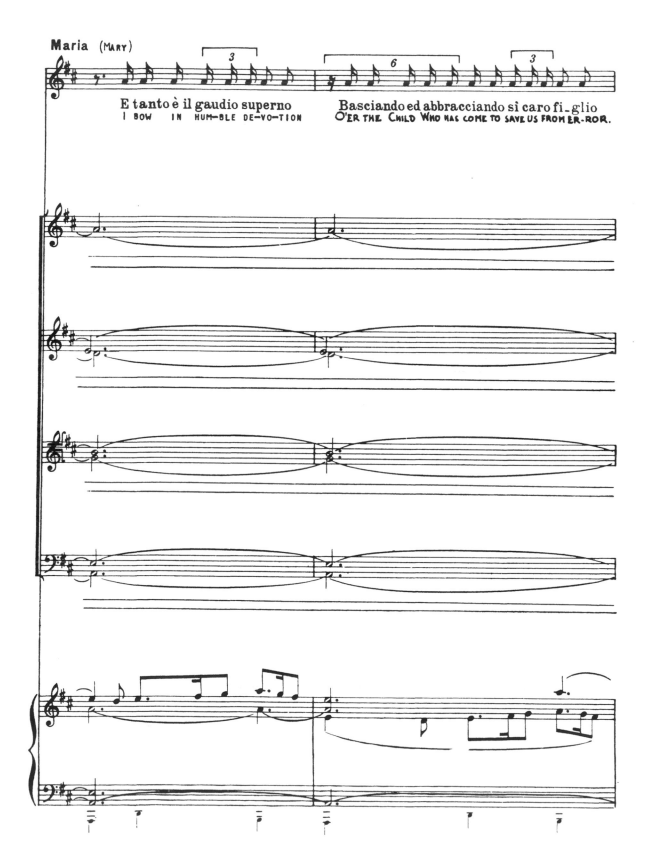

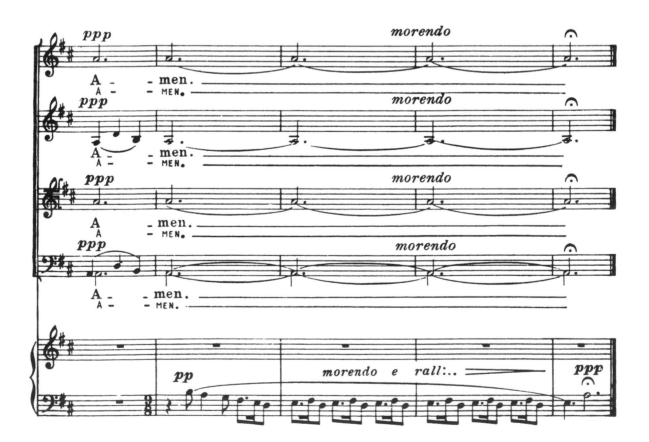